# The Star Maker

**10 Publishing**
a division of **10** of those.com

In the very beginning there was
nothing. Nothing at all.

Except... the Maker. He was there.
He's always been there.

In the beginning the Maker **SPOKE**

And His words were so

that whatever He said,

# HAPPENED.

Just like that.

In the beginning the Maker spoke and...
there were two great lights.

In the beginning, the
Maker made the sun.

In the beginning, the Maker made the moon.

How amazing.
The Maker is so powerful.
He is so clever.

He also made the stars.

How amazing.

The Maker is so powerful. He is so clever.

There are LOTS of stars.

Have you tried to count them?!

There are about 10 billion stars
in the whole universe!

Wow!

The Maker is so powerful. He is so clever.

What a Maker!

One day the Maker stepped down from

His home in Heaven and became... a man!

The Maker became a man.

How extraordinary.

A man... an ordinary-looking man.

In fact, the Star Maker became a little tiny baby. Tiny enough to fit inside a lady's tummy.

Small enough to sleep in an animal's food box.

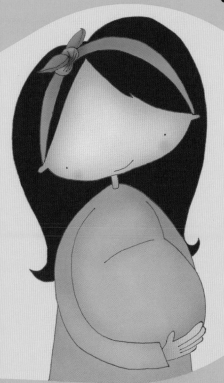

The Maker is Jesus.
Jesus, the Son of God.

Jesus, the Maker of the sun and the moon.

Jesus, the Maker of the stars.

Jesus, who is so powerful. Who is so clever.

Jesus the Star
Maker became a man.

And one of the stars that
He had made shone in the
sky to show where He was.

That star in the sky was
like a giant party popper.
A massive birthday banner.

The Star
Maker is here!

On earth.
God with us.

And so, that very first Christmas, Jesus the Star Maker became a man. A little baby. And the Star Maker lay underneath the star that He had made.

What a thing! How extraordinary.

Why did He do it? Why did the Maker of the stars step down onto the earth?

Why did He say goodbye to His wonderful home in Heaven and come to live among ordinary people? People like us.

Because the Star Maker grew up.
He grew up to do a job.
The Maker who gave up His Heaven,
gave up His life.

He died on a cross.
When Jesus died on that cross He looked weak. He was hurting. People couldn't see that He was the Star Maker.

But it was there on the cross that Jesus was doing something wonderful.

Something amazing.
Something extraordinary.

He was rescuing
His people.

He was making a way
for us to be put right.

To be friends with God Himself.

The Star Maker didn't stay dead.
Death could not hold Him.

# HE CAME ALIVE

Alive forever.

There is no other way.
There was no other plan.
The Star Maker became a man.

In the beginning Jesus spoke.
He made the sun. He made the moon.
He also made the stars.
How amazing. Jesus is so powerful.
He is so clever.

Look up at the stars.
Remember the Star Maker. Jesus.
The Star Maker who was born.
God with us.

Find this story in the Bible in Genesis 1 and Matthew 2.

For Mikey, Dan, Jemima, Bella, Ollie and baby Christmas...

Because we love you.

And because the Star Maker really loves you!

The Star Maker

Text and Illustrations © 2015 Helen Buckley and Jenny Brake.

Published by 10Publishing, a division of 10ofThose Limited.
ISBN 978-1-910587-39-3

Typeset by Diane Warnes.
Printed in the China.

10ofThose Limited, Unit C Tomlinson Road, Leyland, PR25 2DY
Email: info@10ofthose.com
Website: www.10ofthose.com